Seconds

Seconds

Bryan Lee O'Malley

with

Jason Fischer . . . . Drawing Assistant
Dustin Harbin . . . . Lettering
Nathan Fairbairn . . . . Color

BALLANTINE BOOKS
NEW YORK

Published in the United States by Ballantine Books, an imprint of Random House, a division of Random House LLC, a Penguin Random House Company, New York.

BALLANTINE and the HOUSE colophon are registered trademarks of Random House LLC.

Grateful acknowledgment is made to Hal Leonard Corporation for permission to reprint an excerpt from "Over and Over" words and music by Christine McVie, copyright © 1979 by Universal Music-Careers. International copyright secured. All rights reserved. Reprinted by permission of Hal Leonard Corporation.

ISBN 978-0-345-52937-4
Barnes & Noble special edition ISBN 978-0-553-39436-8
Comic-Con International: San Diego special edition (numbered) ISBN 978-0-553-39435-1
Comic-Con International: San Diego special edition (lettered) ISBN 978-0-553-39434-4
eBook ISBN 978-0-345-53878-9

Printed in China on acid-free paper

www.ballantinebooks.com

2   4   6   8   9   7   5   3   1

First Edition

I felt a kind of vertigo, as if
I were merely plunging from
one world to another, and in
each I arrived shortly after
the end of the world had
taken place

—Italo Calvino,
If on a winter's night a traveler

And I said
Could it be me?
Could it really, really be?
Over and over

—Fleetwood Mac

Seconds

She
woke
up,

and
there
was a
glow.

STARE

6

She made a conscious decision not to freak out.

After all, she was clearly dreaming.

AWAKE?

If she were awake, she maybe would have noticed this decrepit room, the rotten blanket, the bare bulb.

AWAKE NOW?

WHO ARE YOU?

Only the dresser was familiar.

SHFF

Or at least

SHFFF

it had been.

There was nothing inside.

Not even socks.

She woke up the next morning remembering none of this.

1

Katie

Katie was stressed out.

I'M PERFECTLY FINE.

She was sleeping too little, worrying too much, feeling old.

SHE WAS IN HER TWENTIES AND YOUNG AND TOTALLY GREAT.

At 29, she felt like everything was slipping away.

UM, NO.

...and she was talking to herself more than usual.

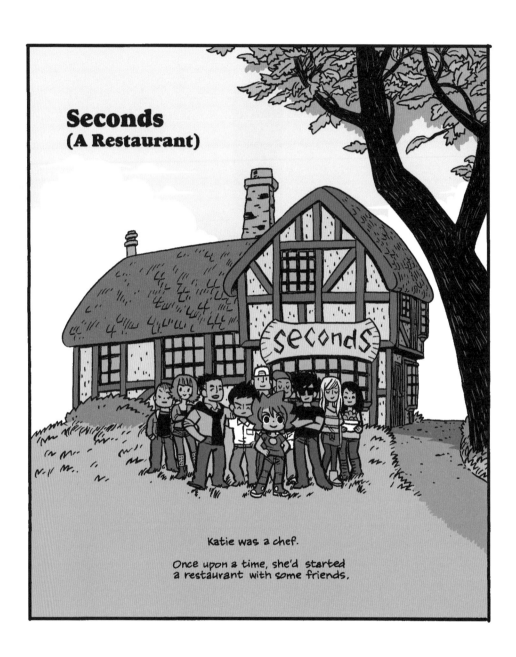

Seconds
(A Restaurant)

Katie was a chef.

Once upon a time, she'd started
a restaurant with some friends.

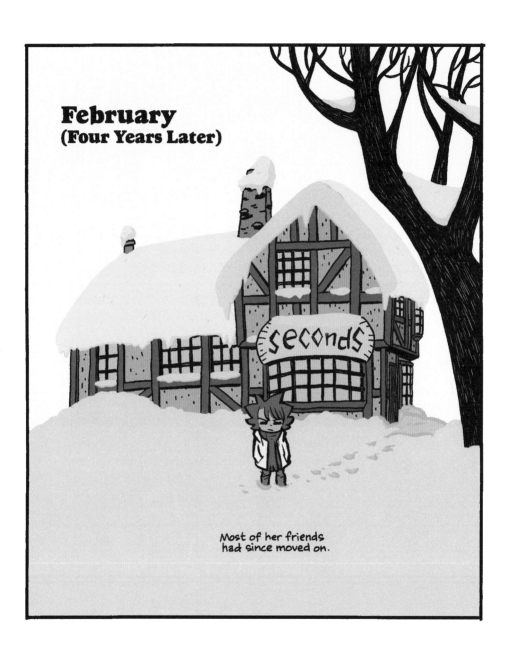

February
(Four Years Later)

Most of her friends
had since moved on.

It was still good. She was still proud of it.

WELCOME TO SECONDS OH IT'S YOU *NEVER MIND THEN*

But she was four years older now, and everyone around her seemed infinitely younger.

The original staff were all gone. The new kids were like a bunch of stylish, sullen babies.

For this and a billion other reasons, Katie was starting a new restaurant.

22 Lucknow Street
(across the river)

Ancient, decrepit, the building had been empty since she was a kid.

It was falling apart, but there'd always been something magical about it all the same.

It would all be real soon. Real and perfect.

She could see it. The space. The light. The happy people.

It wasn't a restaurant yet.

It wasn't anything yet.

I THINK THIS IS ALL GOING REALLY WELL.

THE HELL IT IS.

OKAY, OKAY, IT ISN'T GOING WELL. BUT IT ISN'T GOING POORLY!

Arthur
Katie's new business partner
(34 years old)

I'M TOLD OUR PERMITS ARE DONE. SO THE GUYS ARE ABOUT TO--

DUDE, THIS SUCKS! IT'S TAKING *FOREVER!* WHAT AM I SUPPOSED TO DO?!

KATIE, HOW LONG HAVE YOU BEEN WAITING FOR THIS?

I DUNNO. LIKE FOUR YEARS OR *MY ENTIRE LIFE,* DEPENDING WHERE YOU START COUNTING FROM.

SO WHAT'S A *MONTH?* ANYWAY, AS I WAS--

KATIE.

HM?

phone

OH HEY, I THOUGHT OF A NAME.

FANTASTIC! HIT ME WITH IT. WOW ME. FIRST CUSTOMER RIGHT HERE.

UH,... "KATIE'S."

. . .

WHAT?! IT FITS ON THE SIGN AND EVERYTHING!

I'M JUST AMAZED THAT YOU CAME UP WITH IT ALL BY YOURSELF.

HA HA.

ANYWAY, IT'S YOUR RESTAURANT. YOU'RE THE BOSS AND YOU'RE THE GENIUS, SO WHY NOT HAVE YOUR NAME ON THE SIGN?

IT'S A BOLD MOVE FOR A BOLD PLACE.

YOU ARE *SUCH* A SUCK-UP!

Not that she minded.

19

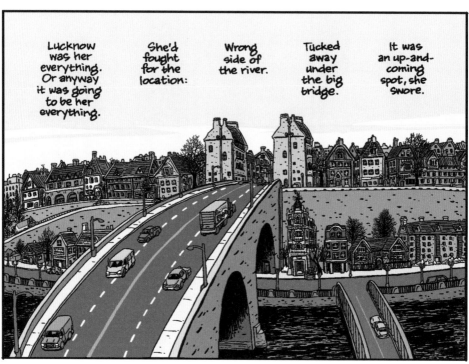

Lucknow was her everything. Or anyway it was going to be her everything.

She'd fought for the location:

Wrong side of the river.

Tucked away under the big bridge.

It was an up-and-coming spot, she swore.

She drove back and forth sometimes four, five times a day.

As if one of these times she'd cross that little bridge and find a finished restaurant.

The waiting was hell.

Seconds had become her purgatory.

At least purgatory had its perks.

PARK

Seconds was probably the most popular restaurant in town.

The food was beloved.

The food was the star here.

And the food was Katie's...

...so Katie was pretty much the star here.

seconds
Executive Chef
Katie Clay

1. sous vide top sirloin
   + foraged green leaves
   + birch ash vinaigrette

2. smoked cornish hen
   + buttermilk mashed tub
   + whipped pork fat
   + pickled asparagus

   roasted spaghetti
   + blistered
   + tomato

23

Max
Katie's ex(?!)

Max was here.

Max was back.

Max smiled.

Katie melted.

Then, slowly, stupidly, she realized that Max was with a girl.

A girl who was preposterously lovely.

And she remembered that he'd left for a reason.

WOW. I GUESS THIS MAKES IT OFFICIAL.

UHH... KATIE, YOU REMEMBER MATILDA.

YOUR SISTER? COME ON. SHE'S LIKE TWELVE.

(DEEPLY UNCOMFORTABLE)

I'M ACTUALLY NINETEEN NOW. HI.

WHAT. NO.

SO, KATIE, UM, IF YOU HAVE A MINUTE, MAYBE WE COULD--

SORRY, BRO, THEY NEED ME DOWNSTAIRS.

I'LL LEAVE YOU IN THE CAPABLE HANDS OF... UH...

HAZEL.

I KNOW YOUR NAME!

← bad boss

KATIE... GIVE ME A CHANCE HERE.

I'M LITERALLY TOO BUSY TO KEEP TALKING.

TIME IS MONEY, MAX!

OH PLEASE!

Katie was an idiot.

WHAT? NO. THAT WAS SO SMOOTH.

Was that really his sister?

Had so much time passed?

WHO EVEN CARES? NOT ME.

Seconds was in an old building, and most of the magic happened down in the basement (purely out of necessity).

For four years she'd dreamed of a bright, airy kitchen, and at Lucknow she'd finally get it.

She really couldn't wait.

SO WHY ARE YOU STILL HERE, KATIE?

Raymond
Co-owner
of Seconds

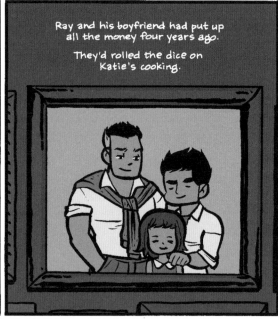

Ray and his boyfriend had put up all the money four years ago.

They'd rolled the dice on Katie's cooking.

Now they owned the best restaurant in town.

And she didn't.

BEST
of the city

"SECONDS"
Best Dinner Spot
3 YEARS
IN A ROW!

So she'd been saving every penny. Living in the same crummy apartment, driving the same crummy car, biding her time.

And she'd done it.

At Lucknow Katie would be an equal partner. Just the thought of it energized her.

(Katie's dorky imagination)

BUT IT'S TAKING SOOO MUCH LONGER THAN I EVER IMAGINED.

AND I JUST

WANNA

COOOOK!

SO *COOK.* YOU'RE THE ONE WHO INSISTED ON LEAVING.

I DON'T WANNA COOK *HERE!* *CHOKED SOB*

THREE MONTHS TRAINING THE NEW GUY AND SCALING YOUR HOURS BACK BIT BY BIT. FINALLY WE'RE PHASING YOUR ASS OUT. YET HERE YOU ARE.

YOU KNOW YOU'RE JUST GETTING IN THE WAY NOW, RIGHT?

OFTEN LITERALLY.

MOAANNN

(IMPORTANT PAPERWORK)

She wasn't chef anymore, or kitchen manager, or really anything. But she still acted like the boss, and the new babies at Seconds treated her accordingly.

She'd hand-picked her successor.

Plucked him from obscurity.

He was young, talented, hard-working. He could have been her protégé. Instead he was... not.

Chef Andrew
(25 years old)

AND WHAT DO WE HAVE HERE?

OH. IT'S GARBAGE.

THIS IS GARBAGE TOO.

YEP... THIS IS ALSO GARBAGE.

HMM THIS IS ALMOST-- OOPS, NO, SORRY, IT'S GARBAGE.

WOW, DUDE.

STARE

TURN THAT RIDICULOUS ASS RIGHT AROUND AND GET THE HELL OUT OF MY KITCHEN BEFORE I *THROW* YOU OUT.

OOH, LOOK AT THE BIG MAN! IT'S *YOUR* KITCHEN NOW? I *BUILT* THIS KITCHEN, BUDDY!

YEAH, AND THEN YOU PUT *ME* IN CHARGE OF IT. YOU OUGHTA KNOW BETTER THAN COME IN HERE AND ACT LIKE YOU DIDN'T.

ANDY, BABY, DON'T GET ME WRONG. I'VE GOT A *TON* OF RESPECT FOR YOUR WORK.

YO! ARE YOU *TOUCHING* MY *GARNISH?!*

MAYBE I AM! WHAT ARE YOU GONNA *DO* ABOUT IT, *HUH??*

33

Even though she wasn't technically Andrew's boss anymore, it still felt wrong.

DON'T REMIND ME.

REMIND YOU OF WHAT?

Max-- well, Max wasn't entirely out of the picture. Max was upstairs. Max had maybe inspired this chain of events.

JUST LET ME ENJOY THIS.

WOW, REALLY? **YOU'RE** SAYING THAT?

NO, I-- SORRY. I'VE JUST GOT A LOT ON MY MIND RIGHT NOW.

PLEASE PROCEED.

WAIT WAIT WAIT. YOU'RE NOT EVEN INTO THIS! YOU DON'T EVEN **DESERVE** THIS!

It always started as a fight. It always ended that way too.

In between, it had its moments.

AAIIIEEEE!!!

This time it was the beginning of something else entirely.

Hazel
(21 years old)

AM I LIKE... OKAY?

YOU'LL BE FINE.

I'VE BEEN THROUGH WORSE.

This was not strictly true. But whatever.

YOU'LL BE FINE.

SIGHH

PHAR

Even though she barely knew the girl, even though Ray knew how much she hated hospitals, here Katie was.

RAY ALSO KNOWS I HAVE NOTHING ELSE WHATSOEVER GOING ON TONIGHT.

twitter

38

Apparently what had happened was this:

UMM, LIKE, I GUESS SHE CAME IN TO GET THE PARSLEY?

Patrick
Line cook
(22 years old)

SOMEONE *(ANDREW)* LEFT IT OVER HERE.

ANDREW'S STATION

BUT IT SHOULD BE *HERE*.

SERVER STATION

AND HAZEL, Y'KNOW, SHE'S SO SKINNY AND QUIET, SHE MUST HAVE SLIPPED IN...

SHE PROBABLY JUST DIDN'T WANT TO BOTHER ME.

I WAS LIKE *JUST* ABOUT TO ASK HER OUT, TOO...

WOULDA BEEN TOMORROW...

YOU'VE BEEN SAYING THAT SINCE HER FIRST DAY, DUDE.

39

They kept Hazel overnight at the hospital (mostly, the doctor said, because she kept fainting at the sight of herself).

Katie had distracted Andrew from his kitchen.

She'd as good as caused the accident.

They both had.

SO *THIS* IS OVER.

NO SHIT THIS IS OVER.

GO HOME, KATIE.

Going home was easy; she lived two floors up. She'd been renting the tiny upstairs apartment from Ray for the past four years.

it must have been three in the morning.

Secon

scroll
scroll
scroll

TOSS

41

How
could
things

have
gone
so
wrong?

SHFF

She'd fallen asleep.

Now, hearing that strangely familiar sound,

she remembered the dream, the girl,

the dresser.

It had been there when she moved in.

Maybe it had always been there.

She used it every day, but tonight it was an alien object.

44

It was empty, like before.

But when she searched one last time,

KLK

? ? ? ? ?

she found the hidden panel, and the little box behind it.

A SECOND CHANCE AWAITS.

1. Write your mistake
2. Ingest one mushroom
3. Go to sleep
4. Wake anew

EVENTS MUST OCCUR ON THESE PREMISES

Contents of the little box:

notebook titled
"MY MISTAKES"

one (1) mysterious red-capped mushroom

immaculately printed instruction card

FLIP

The notebook felt old, like something from an earlier era.

Judging by the heft of it, some of its pages had been removed at some point in the past.

She'd need a pen. And one was there.

SNIC

Her favorite pen. So familiar in her hand. She hadn't seen it since the third day of high school.

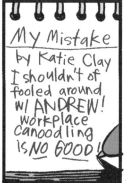

My Mistake
by Katie Clay
I shouldn't of fooled around w/ ANDREW! workplace canoodling is NO GOOD!

FLIP

MY MISTAKES

REVISION #1

She
woke
up,

and
something
had
changed.

2
Hazel

That morning, the girl wasn't at the hospital.

Katie found the girl's address in a three-month-old unread work email (re: new staff).

HAZEL.

HER NAME'S HAZEL.

54

55

Katie's heart wouldn't stop racing.

Was her memory meaningless? Her experience insubstantial?

Was she losing her grip on reality?

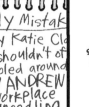

Was she even awake?

57

So, to recap:

Katie ate a mushroom that she'd found in her dresser drawer in the middle of the night

and either she was losing her mind

or she'd changed the universe.

But

Something HAD changed.

THE ACCIDENT *DID* HAPPEN. I *KNOW* IT DID.

The sickening smell of it

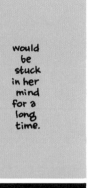

would be stuck in her mind for a long time.

And if the smell was real, the accident was real.

Hazel had burned,

and then she hadn't.

It had been Katie's fault.

BUT NOW IT'S NO-ONE'S FAULT!

Katie had *fixed* it.

She had been given a second chance.

And it seemed like she was the only one who knew.

60

After that, Katie couldn't think of anything better to do with her evening than stalk Hazel.

She quickly realized that Hazel was probably universally hated for the following reasons:

(1) She was way too tall and pretty.

(SHORT)

(2) Her hair was, like, so nice.

(3) Despite being a total fox, she acted like a shy little kid.

HAZEL? UM, YEAH.

IT'S BEEN LIKE THREE MONTHS AND THE OTHER SERVERS HAVEN'T REALLY, UH, WARMED TO HER.

WIPE

IS SHE WEIRD?

SURE. A LITTLE. MAYBE.

61

63

KSHH
KSHH
KSHH

I ADMIRE THAT KIND OF DEDICATION.

ALIVE?

IS IT A RAT?

IT ISN'T REAL.

I MEAN, IT'S A METAPHOR. I REALIZE THAT.

BUT I LIKE THE IDEA OF IT.

Clothes, neatly folded.

WE MAKE THINGS GOOD FOR THEM... THEY MAKE THINGS GOOD FOR US.

IT'S SO SIMPLE.

ANYWAY, I TRY AND DO THINGS BY THE BOOK AROUND HERE.

And... the clothes went on the mantel.

This girl really was weird.

THERE'S A BOOK? ...CAN I BORROW IT?

NO NO NO NO NO, THERE IS NO ACTUAL BOOK.

YEAH, I GOT THAT. "BY THE BOOK." FIGURE OF SPEECH. I WAS JOKING.

OH.

66

MY GRANDMA TOLD A LOT OF STORIES.

I GREW UP WITH THEM.

bread

BUT STORIES ARE *ABOUT* SOMETHING.

KEEPING THE HOUSE SPIRIT HAPPY-- I MEAN, FROM A HISTORICAL PERSPECTIVE--

--IT WAS PROBABLY LIKE SOME KIND OF JUSTIFICATION FOR THE ENDLESS AMOUNTS OF HOUSEWORK THE WOMEN HAD TO DO, RIGHT?

Bread on the rafter.

This was happening.

OKAY. MAKES SENSE.

WHAT HAPPENS IF THE HOUSE SPIRIT *STOPS* BEING HAPPY?

68

69

The next morning,

the fire was still flickering,

and Hazel's clothes

weren't there.

CLANK

No bread. Not a single crumb.

...RATS?

SQUIRRELS?

Did squirrels take the clothes, too?

SHUT UP. I'M THINKING.

72

3
Lis

It felt like she hadn't seen Arthur in a week, which was unusual.

HEY.

WHERE AAARE YOU, DUDE?

I TOLD YOU LIKE FIFTY TIMES.

I KNOW. SORRY. BRAIN BAD.

She suddenly remembered, but only after it was too late.

...FUNERAL.

I... UM... I'M SORRY FOR YOUR... I MEAN... YOU KNOW...

IT IS WHAT IT IS, KATIE. ENOUGH ABOUT ME. I'M FINE. ARE YOU ALRIGHT?

OH... SURE... YEAH. THINGS ARE OKAY...

GREAT. LISTEN, JUST LEAVE THE SITE TO ME, KATIE. EVERYTHING'S FINE. THERE'S NOTHING TO GET ALARMED ABOUT. I'M TAKING CARE OF IT.

771 Talmadge Street

She decided she'd spend the day cooking. It'd keep her busy, calm her nerves, and give her something to show off about later.

At the market, Katie found herself buying like a bushel of mushrooms—she'd been craving them. On the drive back to Seconds she came up with the dish.

She'd made all of it before, but today it came together into a dish she knew was working.

78

Katie brought her new mushroom upstairs.

And stared at it.

82

The girl didn't even act like a person.

More like a cat, or a bird.

WHAT ABOUT A NAME? DO YOU HAVE A NAME?

MY NAME IS KATIE.

YES.

KNOW THIS.

OKAY, STALKER. AND *YOUR* NAME IS...?

LIS.

LIS?

THAT'S YOUR NAME? LIS?

85

I WANT YOU TO GO, LIS. YOU DON'T LIVE HERE, OKAY?

THERE ARE PLACES OUT THERE WHERE YOU CAN GET THE HELP THAT YOU CLEARLY NEED.

YOU SHOULD GO TO ONE OF THEM.

SECONDS IS A RESTAURANT, NOT A...

...CHARITY.

Lis was gone. And as a parting gift, she'd rearranged all of Katie's furniture.

HEY... RAY?

?

HAVE YOU SEEN THIS LIKE SKINNY, WHITE-HAIRED, MAYBE-HOMELESS GIRL HANGING AROUND THE RESTAURANT LATELY?

SHE KINDA HAS... RED EYES. REDDISH.

LIKE SHE'S BEEN DRINKING?

UMMM... NO. NOT REALLY LIKE THAT AT ALL.

KATIE, LET ME PUT YOUR MIND AT EASE.

I HAVE NOT SEEN A WHITE-HAIRED HOMELESS LADY HANGING AROUND.

BUT I ASSURE YOU I WILL KEEP MY EYES PEELED FOR A WHITE-HAIRED HOMELESS LADY NEXT TIME I'M PATROLLING THE AREA FOR UNDESIRABLES.

THANKS.

OH... I GUESS THAT WAS PROBABLY SARCASM? OKAY.

92

93

And then Lis was there.

But Katie dodged nimbly.

HA!

WHAT?

WHAT'S... HAPPENING?

...WHAT IS SHE DOING?

THERE! YOU SEE?

SEE WHAT?

? ? ? ? ?

I DON'T SEE *ANYTHING.*

IS THIS A PRACTICAL JOKE? BECAUSE... I'M VERY GULLIBLE.

GIVE MUSH-ROOM.

ARE YOU KIDDING ME? NO!

PUT MY SHIT BACK WHERE IT BELONGS FIRST!

PUT MY STUFF *BACK,* LIS!!

95

Hazel was still on the bed.

But the bed had moved.

97

IN THE BACK OF MY MIND I KNEW SOMEONE WAS PROBABLY JUST TAKING MY STUFF. I'M NOT AN IDIOT.

BUT I THINK PART OF ME ALWAYS WANTED TO BELIEVE SHE WAS REAL.

HAZEL. I'VE SEEN HER LIKE FOUR TIMES.

SHE'S DEFINITELY REAL.

SO WHY CAN'T *YOU* SEE HER?

SIP

REMEMBER WHEN YOU SAID YOU DO THINGS BY THE BOOK, AND I KNEW IT WAS A FIGURE OF SPEECH, AND WE ALL LAUGHED?

UM... YEAH?

I SECRETLY THOUGHT THERE REALLY WAS A BOOK AND NOW I WISH IT WERE TRUE.

WHO'S THAT?

WHOEVER'S IN CHARGE? LIKE, UM, THE PATRIARCH, USUALLY...

...WELL...

...IN MY GRANDMA'S STORIES, THE HOUSE SPIRIT WOULD ALWAYS APPEAR TO THE MASTER OF THE HOUSE.

...OR THE BOSS.

HEY, RAY, YOU'RE THE BOSS AT SECONDS, RIGHT?

I MEAN YOU'RE IN CHARGE?

ME,,, IN CHARGE,,,?

WELL, HUH...

MAYBE WHEN YOU GET YOUR NEW RESTAURANT GOING...

OR WHEN YOU STOP LIVING HERE.

OR, LIKE... IF YOU *DIED*.

OR... IN BUDDHISM THERE'S A MEASURE OF TIME CALLED A *KALPA* -- IT'S LIKE SIXTEEN MILLION YEARS--

GREAT. THANKS.

YO. BOSS. WANT ME TO MAKE YOU SOME DINNER BEFORE THE RUSH?

PLEASE STOP CALLING ME THAT.

CALLING YOU WHAT? BOSS?

YES.

OK, BOSS.

OK, BOSS.

99

She stepped out for some air, then found herself making an unplanned excursion.

FAST FAST EDDY BURGER™

A long time ago, this had been her favorite restaurant.

DOUBLE CHEESE-BURGER. EXTRA ONIONS, EXTRA MAYO. HOT SAUCE. NO FRIES. WAIT. YES FRIES.

HM, ARE YOU TELLING ME A SECRET? SPEAK UP, PLEASE.

Before she'd started cooking, before her mom had gotten sick, everything had been this easy.

it was like eating an old friend.

CHOMP
CHOMP
CHOMP

URP

100

Katie decided some serious ego-stroking would cap off her evening perfectly.

DOCTOR AND MRS. ANDRETTI! HOW ARE WE DOING TONIGHT?

VERY WELL, THANK YOU, KATIE.

I GOTTA TELL YOU, THIS CHICKEN...

IT'S UNLIKE ANYTHING I'VE EVER TASTED. *DELICIOUS.*

IT'S VERY,.. UM... KATIE?

ARE YOU OKAY?

Max.

KATIE? YOU LOOK A LITTLE FLUSHED.

MAYBE YOU SHOULD SIT DOWN.

KATIE? ...I'M A DOCTOR...

HI.

KATIE! HEY! HAVE YOU MET ADAM?

HI.

hand shake?

wait...

awkward

fist bump

LISTEN, I FEEL BAD ABOUT LAST TIME. WE DIDN'T REALLY GET TO TALK.

YEAH?

YEAH. MAYBE IF YOU HAVE A MINUTE TONIGHT--?

Things had all of a sudden gotten ugly.

WHAT THE HELL WAS WRONG WITH THAT BURGER?!

MOOOAANN

bathroom

NO NO NO NO NO NO

NGA AAA AA

whyyyy??

And after her 147th trip to the toilet, in a haze of nausea and delirium,

she found the little notebook in her hand and began to write.

REVISION #2

DOCTOR AND MRS. ANDRETTI. HI.

HOW'S THE CHICKEN? AMAZING?

THANK YOU.

WHAT?

WHA...?

HEY, MAX.

KATIE! HEY! HAVE YOU MET ADAM?

YEAH, WE MET EARLIER.

WE DID?

HOW YA DOIN', MAX?

UHH...

CONFIDENT!

I'M... GOOD.

LISTEN, I FEEL BAD ABOUT LAST TIME.

UM, YEAH... WE DIDN'T REALLY GET TO TALK.

RIGHT. HERE'S THE THING: I'M A BUSY PERSON.

YOU DON'T EVEN HAVE A MINUTE FOR--

FOR WHAT, MAX?

His smile

faltered.

MAYBE IF YOU WANT TO TALK YOU SHOULD CALL INSTEAD OF, LIKE, STALKING ME, OKAY?

O-OKAY.

106

She left him there   to think about what he'd done.

 And in the morning

  she woke up

 feeling amazing.

4

Rules

JUST SIGN IT RIGHT-- YEAH, THERE.

THANKS.

HELL YEAH!

AUTHORIZA

SO HOW'S IT GOING? SEEMS LIKE WE WERE FURTHER ALONG LAST TIME. HA HA

HA HA. I KEEP TELLING MYSELF SHE'S JUST OLD, BUT EVERY STEP HAS BEEN... TRICKY. FOR EXAMPLE:

WE GO TO PUT YOUR BAR IN, BUT THE FLOOR ISN'T STRAIGHT. JOISTS BELOW US TURN OUT TO BE ROTTEN. BASEMENT'S CAVING IN. FOUNDATION'S CRUMBLING.

SHE'S A BEAST.

HACK OFF ONE HEAD, TWO MORE SHOW UP.

ARTHUR SAID THIS'S YOUR SECOND RESTAURANT. WHERE'S THE OTHER ONE AT?

FIRST AVE.

UP ON THE HILL?

I BEEN THERE. NICE PLACE. GOOD BEER.

THANKS. WHY'S THERE A FIREPLACE HERE?

OH, WE FOUND IT BRICKED UP.

PROBABLY HASN'T SEEN LIGHT FOR SIXTY-ODD YEARS.

IT WAS LIKE A MUMMY'S TOMB IN THERE.

EW. GET RID OF IT. YOU'RE GETTING RID OF IT RIGHT?

HEY, IT'S YOUR BUILDING, LADY.

YOU WANT TO KEEP ANY OF THIS OLD JUNK?

111

And so Katie claimed a treasure from the ancient pile before they dumpstered the whole thing.

It didn't look sixty-odd years old. It looked a *thousand* years old.

Back at Seconds, she went downstairs to show off a little.

..A MUMMY'S TOMB?? WICKED!

WHAT IS THIS THING? A POT?

THE WORD I'D USE IS *CAULDRON*. PRETTY COOL, HUH?

WHAT'S A CAULDRON?

YO, DUMMY. IT'S LIKE AN OLD POT THAT BELONGS TO A WITCH.

..WHAT?

IGNORE THE BABIES, HAZEL. THEY'RE JUST JEALOUS.

JEALOUS OF YOUR BEAUTIFUL HAIR.

THERE'S DIRT IN THE BOTTOM OF YOUR WITCH'S POT.

...DIRT OR ASHES OR SOMETHING, SEE?

113

FWOOF

PAT
PAT
PAT

Some part of her brain thought the ashes might make good fertilizer.

After all,

she was going to need a *lot* of mushrooms.

She started with an even dozen.

117

REVISION #3

REVISION #4

REVISION #5

Even so, her phone chimed with a certain inevitability.

1 new email
Doug (Contractor)

From: Dou
To: Arthur
CC: Katie
Re: Payme

Arthur--

As you kno
project in g

However, t

The bottom line i
**I need $12,000 t
tomorrow.** It's
either that or we
walk.

Sorry. You know
have other iobs

121

Hey Arthur,

I'm seriously freaking out and I really need you to call me.

Hey Arthur,

I'm seriously fre

Hey Arthur,

I just got that email and I was wondering if you're dealing with it, or like, you know, um, if I can help, I guess? I don't mind handling stuff while you're gone! At all. Just let me know!

125

PERSONAL SPACE, LIS.

SMELLS LIKE *MUSH-ROOMS.*

NO MORE.

TOO MANY--

WAIT A SEC!

LUCKNOW--

I COULD CHANGE IT ALL WITH A MUSHROOM! IT'S SO EASY!

WE WOULD HIRE A DIFFERENT CONTRACTOR, FOR STARTERS. THEN I'D GET IN THERE, TWEAK THINGS, *FIX* THINGS.

WHY DIDN'T I THINK OF THIS EARLIER?

NO.

126

MY GOD, LIS, HAVE YOU EVER HEARD OF PANTS?

The mushroom, somehow, remained unchewed.

BLEAH

1. Write you
2. Ingest one m
   3. Go to s
   4. Wake a

EVENTS MUST OCCUR O

EVENTS MUST OCCUR ON THESE PREMISES

Things had to have happened AT Seconds?

Lis hadn't followed her outside. Maybe Lis couldn't follow her outside.

If Lis was the house spirit of Seconds, and the mushrooms were some kind of extension of Lis, it almost made sense.

Katie wiped off the uneaten mushroom, threw it back in the witch's pot, and hid the whole thing in the back seat of her car.

At the very least she knew Lis wouldn't steal her stash.

133

134

OKAY, JUST DO YOUR THING.

1. Sweeping the hearth

KSH KSH

2. Feeding the fire

THEY LIKE TO SLEEP BY THE FIRE, SO I KEEP IT NICE!

3. Clothing drop

I GOT HER A NEW COAT.

ANIMAL PRINT. I DUNNO.

I HOPE SHE LIKES IT.

4. Bread on the rafters

ALWAYS FRESH BREAD, NEVER DAY-OLDS.

PATRICK SAVES ENDS FOR ME.

PLEASE DON'T TELL HIM WHAT I DO WITH THEM...

YOU FEED HER BREAD EVERY DAY? JUST BREAD? WOW.

YEAH... WHY WOW?

I MEAN... UH... WILL SHE GET FAT?

WAIT... BREAD MAKES YOU *FAT?*

135

NOW WHAT?

NOW WE WAIT AND SEE WHAT LIS DOES.

WE MAKE THINGS GOOD FOR HER, SHE MAKES THINGS GOOD FOR US, RIGHT?

RIGHT!

Y'KNOW, THIS WHOLE RITUAL MIGHT BE STUPID, BUT IT STILL MAKES SECONDS FEEL MORE LIKE HOME, EVEN IF--

EVEN IF NOBODY LIKES YOU?

S I P

THEY JUST DON'T KNOW YOU, DUDE.

HOW DO PEOPLE GET TO KNOW PEOPLE?

HELL IF I KNOW.

WHOA... SHHH

136

WHAT?

SHE'S UP THERE. SHE'S EATING THE BREAD.

SHE'S EATING THE BREAD LIKE A SQUIRREL.

OKAY... SHE'S DONE.

THAT WAS SO FAST!

I KNOW. OKAY, SHE'S ON THE MANTEL NOW...

SHE'S PICKING UP THE FUR COAT...

SHE'S...

CHOMP

SNrf

CHEW CHEW

SHOVE

blrkk

WHAT'S SO FUNNY? IS SHE WEARING IT? IS IT UGLY?

WHAT??

ZZZZ

HAHAHA HAHAHA HA HA

140

HE WAS HERE THE OTHER NIGHT...

MAX. HE USED TO WORK HERE.

IS HE YOUR EX?

I GUESS. WE DATED FOR... FOUR YEARS, ALMOST.

FOUR YEARS? WHAT HAPPENED?

IT'S... COMPLICATED.

BUT WHY'D HE COME IN? 'CAUSE HE MISSED YOU?

I DON'T EVEN KNOW WHAT HE EVER SAW IN ME.

141

HE WAS A FRIEND OF RAY'S, AND I JUST NEEDED GENERAL KITCHEN HELP, SO HE WAS IT.

(Max, five minutes before his first shift)

I HATED HIM AT FIRST. HE WAS LIKE ANDREW TIMES A BILLION. SUCH HOT SHIT. LEATHER JACKET, BLONDE ON HIS ARM. AND HE COULD BARELY COOK.

BUT WE COULD *TALK*. WE WORKED TOGETHER EVERY NIGHT AND THE CONVERSATION NEVER ENDED.

SO YEAH, ME AND MAX HOOKING UP WAS INEVITABLE.

HE GOT BETTER IN THE KITCHEN. WE MADE EACH OTHER STRONGER.

WHEN SECONDS GOT POPULAR WE HAD TO HIRE NEW LINE COOKS AND START SPLITTING THE WEEK.

Andrew (TRAINEE)

WE NEVER SAW EACH OTHER ANYMORE. THAT GOT HARD.

AND I GUESS WHAT WE HAD WASN'T THAT STRONG.

142

BUT... WHAT *HAPPENED?*

UGH... I DON'T KNOW.

EMPTY

HE WANTED ME TO MOVE IN WITH HIM, BUT I WAS SAVING SO MUCH MONEY BY LIVING UPSTAIRS...

WE STARTED RESENTING EACH OTHER ABOUT WORK, AND, AND...

I GUESS IT *IS* COMPLICATED.

NO, IT ISN'T. IT'S... I DIDN'T TELL HIM.

I DIDN'T TELL HIM ABOUT MY NEW RESTAURANT. I THOUGHT IT'D FALL APART. I COULDN'T CONVINCE MYSELF IT WAS REAL. THEN HE FOUND OUT FROM SOMEONE ELSE, AND THAT WAS IT. HE WALKED.

Snf *(drunk)*

HAZEL...

LIS GAVE ME MUSHROOMS.

143

WHAT?

SHE GAVE ME SPECIAL MUSHROOMS AND I'VE BEEN EATING THEM.

THEY CHANGE THINGS, HAZEL.

BUT NOT EVERYTHING. JUST WHAT HAPPENS *HERE.*

ADULT LIFE IS TERRIBLE, HAZEL. NEVER GROW UP.

EVERYTHING'S COMPLICATED, AND THERE ARE TOO MANY RULES, AND YOU CAN ONLY CHANGE THINGS THAT--

WAIT! WHOA.

I COULD USE A MUSHROOM TO TELL MAX!

OUR WHOLE RELATIONSHIP HAPPENED RIGHT HERE.

I COULD FIX IT.

...

144

The next thing she knew, she was writing. Writing about Max.

REVISION #6

ALL GOOD, KAY?

HEY.

I LITERALLY JUST HAD THIS IDEA.

OH?

I... WOULD LIKE TO OPEN A SECOND RESTAURANT.

IS THIS YOUR WAY OF ASKING ME TO BE A PART OF IT?

And even here, in this perfect weird fugue state...

... she had to suppress a surge of panic.

...Y-YEAH!

YEAH, OF COURSE!

146

What
was
this?

What
was
she
seeing
now?

She
didn't
like
it at
all.

147

And
when
she
woke
up,

there
he
was.

5
Max

She woke him up the rest of the way.

Meanwhile, Katie took stock of her new and improved life.

WHAT THE HELL...?

Her home had become strange and boy-centric.

Max *lived* here.

Max *lived* here?

WE LIVE... ...TOGETHER?

Lis wasn't happy.

But Katie didn't even notice.

152

Katie was busy flipping out.

A boy lived in her house, and his shit was everywhere.

The giant TV. The mess. Video games??

IT'S LIKE I DON'T EVEN KNOW HIM!

When had Max ever once in his life played a guitar?

DO ALL BOYS PLAY GUITAR?

TWANG

Where was her favorite chair? Why'd they have his gross old couch?

Half the wardrobe was suddenly his clothes.

T-shirts and work shirts and jeans and blazers and all of it enormous.

WAIT... WHERE'S THE REST OF MY STUFF?

She buried her face in it.

I LOVE THE SMELL! I LOVE IT!!

(Or maybe she was taking deep breaths to avoid hyperventilating.)

NO.

She dressed cute.

She felt newly confident.

She felt cool.

She pushed away her questions and confusion.

This was good. It was just good.

HI.

HI...

KATIE. REALLY?

MMM. MMMAX. MAX MAX MAX MAX MAX.

WE HAVE WORK, KATIE.

BUT *MAAAX!!!*

154

Max went straight for the driver's side.

Her car keys were already in his pocket.

No-one but her had ever driven that car before.

This was love, right?

Love couldn't be a bad thing.

155

156

Lucknow
was a wreck.

It was like
progress had
reversed.

Something was crushing her. Some unseen force. She could barely stand. This was insanity.

It had gotten worse.

She slowly realized Max was talking to the guy without her.

YOU GOTTA GIVE US A FEW DAYS, DOUG.

OUR PARTNER IS OUT OF TOWN. YOU KNOW THAT.

$18,000, BUDDY. OR I'M GONE.

EIGHTEEN?! IT WAS *TWELVE* YESTERDAY!

IT WAS ALWAYS EIGHTEEN, LADY, BUT THAT'S A MOOT POINT BECAUSE I DON'T SEE YOU PAYING ME SO I GUESS I'LL SEE YOU IN *HELL*.

158

YOU...

YOU PIECE OF HUMAN GARBAGE

I WILL FUCK YOU UP

KATIE. SETTLE.

KEEP HER IN CHECK, MAX.

WATCH ME PULL UP THE EMAIL YOU SENT LAST NIGHT, **DOUG!!**

CALL ME A LIAR...

bottom line
ed **$18,000**
rrow. It's
r that or w

She remembered it. She *remembered* it.

. . .

It had changed.

159

What else had changed?

What was happening to her?

IF YOU GET THE FUNDS, GIVE ME A CALL.

YOU AND YOUR WIFE HAVE A NICE DAY.

WIFE?! EXCUSE ME, YOU SEXIST DICK--

WE'RE *MARRIED* NOW?!

So Katie didn't have a restaurant. She had a shell. She had a husk.

At least she had Max now.

Her god damn husband.

He'd managed to get Arthur on the phone.

He was keeping his voice down.

Excluding her.

Taking care of things.

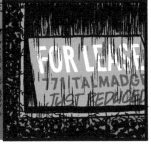

FOR LEASE
771 TALMADGE
JUST REDUCED

Just like she'd wanted.

It seemed that Seconds would continue to be Katie's purgatory.

She was in no mood to interact with humans, but Max dragged her around to the front door.

OH, UH... WELCOME TO SECONDS, BUT WE'RE ACTUALLY NOT OPEN YET--

MAX!!

HEY, GUYS!

MAAAAX! WE NEVER SEE YOU ANYMORE!

WE MISS YOU, MAX!

They loved him.

Why did they love him?

Why did they love him and not *her*?

162

She didn't know this photo.

She had no memory of this day.

She hadn't lived it.

HEY.

EVERYTHING OKAY?

EVERYTHING? NO.

IS HE AROUND?

WHO, MAX? HE WENT UPSTAIRS TO MAKE SOME CALLS.

COOL.

SMOOCH

CLUTCH

WHAT ARE YOU DOING?!

WHAT DO YOU MEAN WHAT AM I DOING?

I... I'M *MARRIED,* ANDREW.

WE CAN'T KEEP DOING THIS!

COME ON, KATIE. THAT NIGHT WE SHARED-- YOU FELT IT TOO.

What night? She'd erased that night.

I *ERASED* THAT NI-- I MEAN *THAT NIGHT NEVER HAPPENED!*

YOU CAN PRETEND ALL YOU WANT, KATIE.

YOUR HEART KNOWS WHAT'S UP.

THAT'S... SO CHEESY...

Had some other version of the night she'd spent with Andrew taken place in her new married life?

Or... had this changed in some other way?

SHHH. I'M JUST GONNA GO WITH IT.

AHEM.

SUPER CASUAL

SO, YOU REDUCE THE WINE AND BROTH FOR...

KATIE. COME IN FOR A SEC.

165

WHAT'S UP, RAYMOND? WE WERE JUST, UM--

OH *STOP*. I KNOW ABOUT YOU AND ANDREW.

. . .

I MEAN *WHAT* ABOUT US? BECAUSE WE WERE REALLY ONLY--

KATIE. EVERYONE KNOWS. EVERYONE BUT MAX, I MEAN.

AND THE ONLY REASON HE *DOESN'T* KNOW IS BECAUSE HE'S BEEN SO BUSY WITH HIS NEW RESTAURANT.

UH, IT'S ACTUALLY *MY* NEW RESTAURANT.

BUT YOU SEE WHAT I'M SAYING, KATIE.

I DON'T KNOW THAT I DO, RAY.

I'M SAYING STOP. YOU AND ANDREW. WHATEVER IT IS. JUST STOP.

PLEASE. IT'S DISRESPECTFUL. TO MAX. TO EVERYONE.

OH. OH, THAT.

166

HAZEL!

LET'S TALK! CAN WE TALK? I NEED TO TALK.

GAK. HI...

WHAT'S UP? WHAT ARE YOU UP TO? HOW ARE YOU?

UM... I'M A BIT EARLY FOR MY SHIFT, SO I WAS GONNA GO OUT AND DO SOME SHOPPING...

COOL! SOUNDS GOOD!

. . . .

SHE'S WEARING HEELS EVEN THOUGH SHE'S ALREADY TALL

HOW IS THAT FAIR?

167

YEAH-- YOUR WEDDING VOWS, AND DANCING TO YOUR SONG, AND--

WHAT? *NO!*

WE TALKED ABOUT HOW MY RELATIONSHIP WAS A *MESS.* MAX *LEFT* ME.

BUT AFTER WE TALKED, I ATE ONE OF LIS'S MUSHROOMS AND ALL OF IT CHANGED!

· · ·

WOW...

...THEY RAISED THEIR PRICES.

ARE YOU LISTENING TO ME?!

169

I WANT TO SEE THE MAGIC MUSHROOM PATCH! IS IT LIKE A FAIRY RING?

UMM...

I THINK IT'S SAFEST IF I DON'T-- LIKE, YOU KNOW--

IF THEY FELL INTO THE, UM, WRONG HANDS--

OH GOSH! YOU'RE RIGHT!

I KNOW. I'M SO SORRY.

LYING

I GUESS THERE'S ONE QUESTION ON MY MIND.

IF WE ASSUME SHE USES THE MUSHROOMS TO CHANGE LITTLE THINGS FOR US EVERY DAY...

... WHY WOULD SHE START LETTING *YOU* CHANGE *BIG* THINGS?

Katie suddenly remembered the first thing. The accident.

But it didn't seem appropriate to tell Hazel about that.

171

HOW WAS YOUR DAY?

UM, CONFUSING AND TERRIBLE. HOW WAS YOURS?

...SO YOU THINK SPIKE'S THIS TOTAL BAD GUY, BUT IN SEASON SEVEN, HE SHOWS HIS TRUE--

...ARE YOU LISTENING?

Back in the basement, Katie noticed that the office door was ajar...

SIGH

Max
(29 years old)
Status: bummed

GRAB

spl ish

clink!

SIP

173

THIS IS THE ROOM WHERE WE MET.

YOU WERE SO COOL.

I WAS ONLY PLAYING IT COOL 'CAUSE *YOU* WERE SO COOL.

PSSH.

NO, REALLY.

YOU HAD YOUR OWN KITCHEN. I WAS BUMMING AROUND. WASTING MY TIME.

I RESPECTED THE HELL OUT OF YOU BEFORE I EVER WALKED IN HERE, KATIE.

IT'S TAKEN ME THIS LONG TO EVEN BEGIN TO CATCH UP.

He'd never opened up like this before.

It was like she'd tricked her way into a deeper relationship without having to do any of the heavy lifting. Pretty awesome!

THIS IS ALSO THE ROOM WHERE WE DECIDED ON LUCKNOW.

LAST FALL. REMEMBER? US AND ARTHUR.

LOOKING THROUGH THOSE REAL ESTATE PORTFOLIOS. MAKING THE WRONG CHOICE.

174

OH, DUDE, NO. NO NO. IT IS WHAT IT IS.

WHAT'S DONE IS DONE. WE... WE MOVE FORWARD, RIGHT?

ARTHURISMS.

HE'S OUT OF TOWN. SOMEONE'S GOTTA SAY 'EM.

NAH. FACE IT, KAY, LUCKNOW'S A MONEY PIT.

WE BLEW IT.

IF WE'D PICKED TALMADGE, I BET WE'D BE IN THERE RIGHT NOW, COOKING UP A STORM.

Lucknow had been Katie's choice.

In her version of that day, it'd been just her and Arthur in the room. She'd insisted on Lucknow.

She'd probably argued just as hard with Max in this version.

But why? What did it all add up to? Nothing. Her past self was clearly a pretentious idiot.

Was Max right?

Had she blown it?

177

182

It was a tree.

At the junctures of its branches, she saw points of light.

Seconds was nestled in the branches, tiny and perfect.

Then it was gone.

She spotted it again, somewhere else this time.

Lis was trying to show her something.

This meant something.

SHFFf

Whatever that was, it was kind of amazing.

Katie was kind of awed and kind of astonished.

On the other hand, she had no idea what any of that awesome and astonishing shit was supposed to mean.

She was tired, and confused, and tired of being confused, and so...

CHOMP

CHEW CHEW CHEW

187

GULP

She hid under the covers. But in like a defiant and cool way.

SHUT UP.

REVISION #7

YOU OKAY, BABY?

HMM... WELL, IF THERE'S A SCARY MONSTER DOWN IN THE KITCHEN, I'M NOT SURPRISED IT'D BE YOU, BABY.

THANKS...

HOWEVER, IF WE ANALYZE YOUR DREAM FROM A PSYCHOLOGICAL STANDPOINT, IT'S CLEARLY ALL ABOUT--

SHUT UP!

WHOMP

MMF MRPH MAH MF

She loved him. Or something.

I DO. I REALLY DO.

She felt safe in his arms. She needed him now.

The restaurant, the house spirit-- right now none of it was as important to her as Max.

Her god damn husband.

YOU DO WHAT?

SHH.

194

Now Max was like *upset* or something. "Their" new restaurant?

How was Katie supposed to know which semantics were off limits in a relationship that was a mystery to her?

It was *her* restaurant. It wasn't for sharing.

SO... THINGS ARE GOING WELL AT TALMADGE?

I GUESS *"WE"* MADE THE RIGHT CHOICE?

Nothing. He gave her the silent treatment the whole way.

Which didn't bother her. She could fix him later if needed.

196

Under budget.
Under schedule.

Talmadge was
almost finished.

The bastards
had been right.

She gawked at the perfect wall sconces.

the ideal tiles,

the bar she'd dreamed about,

all the precious shit she'd wanted.

But...

... the layout was wrong.

Where was the ridiculously amazing chandelier she'd picked out?

BORING

And why was this color going on the walls right now?

HIDEOUS

She'd given up Lucknow. She'd gotten this instead. All for a guy.

SHUDDER TO THINK

HIM

Was he worth it?

WHAT? YES!

OF... OF COURSE HE WAS.

Graphic Designer(?)

MAX, KATIE, GREAT TO SEE YOU AGAIN!

HEYYY! C'MERE! HOW *ARE* YOU? HOW'S ALEX?

TOUSLING HER HAIR LIKE OLD PALS →

She'd never seen this person before in her life.

?

The woman had met Katie before. Just not *this* Katie.

IT'S BEEN TOO LONG!

S-SURE HAS!

SO, YOU GUYS HAVE BEEN PRETTY CLEAR ON WHAT YOU WANTED ALL ALONG.

TODAY I'VE GOT SOME ROUGH CONCEPTS FOR US TO GO OVER!

Admittedly, Katie had gotten this far in the process mostly due to spacetime shenanigans.

But she was here now, and she'd make the best of it--

THIS IS EXCITING!

MKII

MKII

MKII

MKII

...

They all said "MK II"...

What the hell was this?

THEY ALL SAY MKII...

There had to be some kind of mistake.

I SURE HOPE SO!

HEY... WHAT HAPPENED TO CALLING IT "KATIE'S"?

I LIKE THE LOGO WE PICKED.

Last fall. Last fall was too far. The farther back she went, the more wide-ranging the ramifications of her changes.

AND MKII IS A GOOD NAME. I THINK IT'S STRONG.

She tried to imagine another Katie, a Katie who thought "MKII" was a good name for a restaurant. Where was she now? When had she given up on life?

MAX AND KATIE'S SECOND RESTAURANT. IT'S CLEVER.

I KNOW IT ISN'T EXACTLY WHAT YOU WANTED.

What was the precise moment at which the two Katies had diverged?

BUT YOU NEED TO COMPROMISE ONCE IN A WHILE, Y'KNOW?

UM, WHERE ARE WE GOING?

They were going to Lucknow. She had to see what was happening at Lucknow.

201

It was a ruin.

It'd always been there, as far back as she could remember. Old, junky, run-down. But never like this.

This seemed beyond repair. Unsalvageable.

LOOK AT THIS DUMP. WE MADE THE RIGHT CHOICE.

Y-YEAH...

Had she caused this?

Where was she?

202

UMM...
I'LL BE
RIGHT
IN.

SURE.

She'd decided to bring the mushrooms inside.

Their presence in her car was starting to freak her out.

She didn't realize, however,

that one mushroom remained, lost in the back seat.

203

204

Katie stashed the witch's pot in the back of her nightstand.

She couldn't see Lis anywhere.

But Lis was there.

And after, when she went back downstairs,

Katie got turned around between the stairs and the kitchen, which was weird--

--it's not like the hallway was a maze.

205

206

YOU'RE SUCH A HYPOCRITE, KATIE.

I'M WHAT?

YOU'RE USING ME.

I'M **WHAT?**

YOU'RE MY BOSS AND YOU'RE OLDER AND YOU'RE MARRIED AND--

OLDER?! WHAT DOES THAT HAVE TO DO WITH ANYTHING?

OH COME ON. I'M NOT AN IDIOT.

YOU **ARE** AN IDIOT. WE WERE JUST HAVING FUN. BOTH OF US.

AND IT **STOPPED** BEING FUN, DUDE.

OKAY. YEAH! I **AM** AN IDIOT.

'CAUSE I **RESPECT** YOU. I WANTED TO WORK HERE BECAUSE OF YOU. YOUR FOOD.

BUT I'M NOTHING TO YOU.

WHAT?

LIKE THAT FUCKING-- THAT GIRL HAZEL? WHY HER?

WHY CAN'T YOU TALK TO *ME* LIKE THAT? I WANTED US TO BE FRIENDS.

DUDE. ANDREW... I DIDN'T KNOW YOU FELT LIKE--

I GOTTA GO.

WHAT? HANG ON A SEC!

I DON'T LIKE IT BACK HERE ANYMORE. THE WALK-IN... YOU DON'T FEEL THAT?

FEEL WHAT?

I DON'T KNOW. NEVER MIND.

But she did feel it.

The shadow. She knew it was real.

I DON'T FEEL ANYTHING.

Um, yeah, she did, actually.

208

When she got upstairs, Max was getting his jacket on to leave.

WHERE ARE YOU GOING?

OUT.

HEY, ARE YOU STILL PISSED ABOUT THE WHOLE "NAMING THE RESTAURANT AFTER ME" THING?

BECAUSE IT WAS A JOKE, OKAY?

NAH.

IT'S FINE.

SCARY FAKE SMILE

IT IS?

OH... OKAY...

WELL...

BYE...

There seemed to be a distinct possibility that it was not fine.

209

As she watched, the nightstand moved on its own, waddling toward the end of the bed.

THIS IS *SO* DUMB.

HOP

211

212

VANISH!

...What?

What was it?
What caused
Lis to react
so violently?

Was it the
witch's pot?

...WHY?

There were six mushrooms in the pot.

How many changes had she made now?

She tried to do the math, but immediately gave up.

toss

214

REVISION #8

HEY, AREN'T WE MEETING THAT GRAPHIC DESIGNER TODAY?

HEY, THAT'S RIGHT!

I'M JUST *SO* EXCITED ABOUT *OUR* NEW RESTAURANT, BABY.

MMM. YEAH.

WOW, EVERYTHING IS PERFECT AND I LOOOVE IT!

UGLY

UGLY

MKII! I LOVE THIS! WHAT DO YOU THINK, HONEY?

She'd only had to write herself a minor attitude adjustment first thing in the morning. The rest took care of itself.

Andrew blindsided her again-- Katie had completely forgotten about this.

Oh well.

I'M NOTHING TO YOU!

At the end of the day, Max still loved her, and that was the important thing.

She woke up in a cold sweat, moaning non-words in a weird, strangled voice.

That day she couldn't shake the image of that terrible shadow in the walk-in. Something very wrong was happening.

It was growing. She could swear it was growing.

217

REVISION #9

And like that, the day was over, and she could barely remember what she needed to change for tomorrow.

They had started cooking, hammering out the details of their new menu. Every moment should have been a delight, but somehow none of them were.

Max was always disappointed in her, as if she'd been perfect once. As if he was now.

Four left.

She could get it right with four more. No problem.

REVISION #10

PANT
PANT
PANT
PANT

SHH. IT'S OKAY.

And Max was there.

And she just started sobbing.

221

Katie fell asleep again.

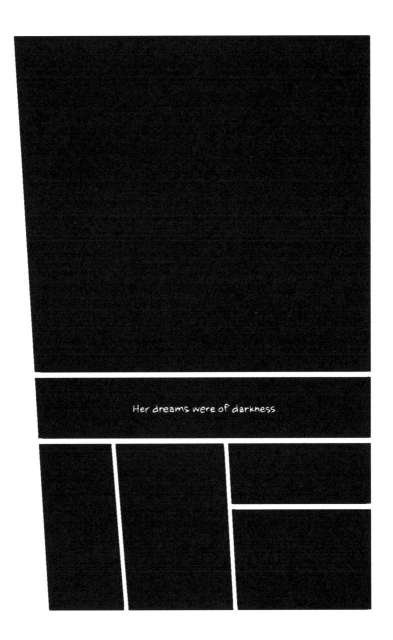

Her dreams were of darkness.

She
woke
up,

and there
was a glow.

224

6
Control

When Katie woke up, she was back in her normal bedroom with Max asleep beside her.

She decided to take an early-morning drive. Away from here.

She ended up at Hazel's house.

She wondered: was there a house spirit here too?

It seemed rude to barge in, so she texted.

Are you home?

BZZ

?

Like are you at home

BZZ

yes

Ok I'm coming in

BZZ

what

231

SHF
SHFF

SO I GUESS YOU'VE BEEN... UH... PRETTY BUSY?

YEAH. THINGS HAVE BEEN KINDA... BAD-ISH?

MAN, YOU HAVE A *LOT* OF CLOTHES.

She wanted to tell Hazel everything. But she couldn't keep track of what she'd already said, of what had or hadn't happened, of what she even knew anymore.

THE OTHER NIGHT, WHAT DID YOU WANT TO TALK ABOUT?

OH... UM...

NOTHING.

A few days of friendship neglect and things were this awkward already.

OH! I FOUND THIS OLD PICTURE BOOK IN THE ATTIC--

I DON'T KNOW IF IT'S FROM WHEN I WAS A KID, OR WHEN MY MOM WAS, OR--

MY AUNT USED TO READ IT TO ME. I CAN'T BELIEVE I FORGOT ALL ABOUT IT!

GOOD HOUSE, BAD HOUSE.

I THINK I CHEWED OFF THAT CORNER...

GOOD HOUSE, BAD HOUSE

THIS IS CREEPY FEEL'N... IT LOOKS *JUST* LIKE SECONDS!

NO IT DOESN'T. SETTLE DOWN.

OKAY, SO THERE'S THIS FAMILY AND THEY JUST MOVED TO A NEW HOUSE.

BUT ONLY THE LITTLEST DAUGHTER REALIZES THEY ACCIDENTALLY BROUGHT THEIR OLD HOUSE SPIRIT ALONG.

I GUESS HE WAS SLEEPING IN THIS OLD TRUNK.

234

OF COURSE, THERE'S A HOUSE SPIRIT IN THEIR NEW HOUSE TOO.

SO THE TWO HOUSE SPIRITS FIGHT OVER THE HOUSE.

IT'S, LIKE, FUNNY? BUT... KINDA DARK.

THE FAMILY CAN'T KEEP BOTH SPIRITS HAPPY, 'CAUSE DIFFERENT THINGS MAKE THEM HAPPY.

EVERY HOUSE SPIRIT WANTS TO LIVE IN A DIFFERENT KIND OF HOUSE, I GUESS.

ANYWAY, THE FAMILY TRIES EVERYTHING, BUT IN THE END THIS HOUSE "GOES BAD."

235

236

I'VE BEEN WORKING EXTRA HARD TO KEEP LIS HAPPY, BUT IT ISN'T HELPING.

AND I THINK...

I THINK *THIS* IS WHAT'S HAPPENING.

GOOD HOUSE, BAD HOUSE

WHAT?

YOU MEAN THAT BOOK FOR LITTLE BABIES?

THE TWO HOUSE SPIRITS THING?

. . .

LIKE... AT SECONDS? IN REAL LIFE?

...HOW?

I THINK YOU INVITED SOMETHING IN.

237

The door. The shadow.

She knew it was real. She'd known all along.

She'd invited it into her home. It didn't matter how or why.

What mattered was that she had to face it. And she was ready.

She was almost ready.

She was getting there.

She walked
with purpose.
For like a
second.

The kitchen
seemed
farther than
ever. The
halls kept
stretching.

The basement
was changing,
evolving, with
every revision.
Katie hadn't
caused this--

--it
had.

And then

things
went

HEY,
CHEF.

way
past
weird.

241

They were skeletons.

Skeletons were working in her kitchen.

DISHWASHER

HEY, BOSS.

PREP COOK

HEY, BOSS.

FOOD RUNNER

...

PATRICK

HEY, BOSS.

!!!!!

242

KATIE...!

HEY...

. . .

WE NEED TO TALK.

Talk? They needed to flee. Run for their lives.

The hallways around them were dark and twisting and hot as a furnace and filled with skeletons and everyone was acting like this was normal.

This was reality.

TALK?

...ABOUT WHAT?

WELL, I THOUGHT ABOUT IT A LOT, AND...

KATIE, COULD YOU MAYBE LOOK AT ME FOR LIKE FIVE SECONDS?

B-BUT HE'S--

Smiling?

...or just a skull?

HE'S *WHAT*? A *SKELETON*? GET OVER YOURSELF, DUDE.

LISTEN... I REALIZED YOU'RE RIGHT.

I AM?

WE'RE NEVER GONNA BE FRIENDS, KATIE.

AND WHATEVER PHYSICAL ATTRACTION THERE WAS BETWEEN US IS OVER.

WHAT? I DIDN'T SAY THAT.

I DIDN'T SAY EITHER OF THOSE.

I STILL THINK--

244

NO. LISTEN. I PUT IN MY NOTICE WITH RAY.

YOU WHAT?

I'M MOVING ON.

SO ONE WAY OR ANOTHER, THIS, US--

--IT'S OVER, KATIE.

And Max was there.

And Max had heard everything.

Things were bad.

Things couldn't really be worse.

But she could still fix it.

She just needed to use a mushroom right away.

Three left.

Three was enough.

But then she couldn't find the little notebook.

HEY... ARE YOU LOOKING FOR SOMETHING IN THERE?

BECAUSE I FOUND SOMETHING. AND I THINK IT BELONGS TO YOU.

He had it.

MY MISTAKES

Max had her mistakes in his hot little hand.

So... things were worse.

WHAT IS THIS, KATIE?

WHAT THE HELL IS IT?

Oh no.

OH NO.

I THOUGHT IT WAS LIKE A DIARY AT FIRST.

SOME KIND OF WEIRD, GUILTY DIARY.

My Mistake
by Katie Clay
I shouldn't of
fooled around
w/ ANDRE
workplace
canoodling
is NO GOOD.

Oh no no no.

NO

She had to get it back.

BUT... YOU READ ON AND IT'S FULL OF MADE-UP GARBAGE.

COND CHANCE AWAITS

1. Write your mistake
2. Ingest one mushroom
3. Go to sleep
4. Wake anew

UNREALITY.

VERY DETAILED UNREALITY.

ALSO, YOUR SPELLING IS ATROCIOUS...

The rules were unspecific. Write your mistake?

They didn't even mention the notebook.

rite your mistake
gest one mushroom
3. Go to sleep
4. Wake anew

No time for sleep. No time for rules.

CHOMP

KATIE!

BAM BAM

BAM BAM

KA--

REVISION #11

Katie changed her sweater,

just so she could take the last two mushrooms.

and keep them with her.

1 2

She couldn't let them out of her sight. The stakes were too high now.

Then she headed

254

???????

255

The state of the dining room did not dispel this notion.

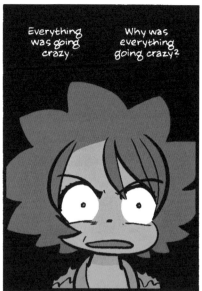

Everything was going crazy.

Why was everything going crazy?

Why would there be a band at her restaurant?

Were they really skeletons, or was she seeing things?

...HOW IS A SKELETON PLAYING A WOODWIND?

HEY, BOSS!

WHAT THE HELL ARE YOU WEARING?

WHAT THE HELL ARE THEY ALL WEARING?

UM... WHAT'S GOING ON?

WELL, THIS IS A *RESTAURANT*, AND THESE PEOPLE ARE HERE FOR A "MEAL"...

I MEAN WHY ARE THE SERVERS DRESSED LIKE... *THAT?*

WHAT, NOW YOU DON'T LIKE THE UNIFORMS? YOU HELPED PICK THEM, KATIE.

I GUESS I HELPED HIRE ALL THOSE SKELETONS IN THE KITCHEN TOO?

HELPED? NO. THE SKELETONS WERE 100% YOU, CHEF.

YOU CAN SEE THEM TOO?!

YOU'RE STARTING TO WORRY ME, KATIE.

259

The kitchen was hot and dark and impossibly far from the stairs.

And Max was back.

And he smiled, because he loved her again.

Because he didn't remember what had happened.

Because what had happened hadn't happened.

260

She loved him, and he loved her, and that was all that mattered now.

The other stuff was--

She'd only
blinked.

I
LOVE
YOU,
MAXY
BABY.

I
LOVE
YOU
TOO,
YANA
BABY.

I
LOVE
YOU
TOO.

MAX.

No.

263

This wasn't Max cheating.

It hadn't just happened.

It was war.

THE LAST MUSHROOM

... OH, HEY. WHERE *IS* EVERYONE? I'M SLAMMED HERE!!

I NEED FOUR RIBEYES FROM THE WALK-IN, OKAY?

MAX...?

Even moments later, Hazel couldn't say with certainty that she'd seen Lis, or anything at all.

Either way, it was time to get the hell out of Seconds. Maybe never to return.

Hazel sat still and silent the whole way,

clinging to the old storybook like a lifeline.

GOOD HOUSE BAD

Snow fell thick and fast. Everything outside her car was blank, white,

as if the world

was being erased.

277

7

Can't Go Back

The witch's pot.

If she could find it, if she could bring it back--

IT'D FIX EVERYTHING!

...well... Maybe it'd help, anyway.

First of all, she had to get Hazel home safely.

I MUST HAVE TAKEN A WRONG-- HMM.

UM, HAZEL...? WHERE DO YOU LIVE?

I DON'T... KNOW.

blink

GOOD HOUSE, BAD HOUSE

And like that, she was at the start again,

a little bit closer to the end.

283

LET'S

FIGHT.

SHFFF

PCHOOM

BAM

LIS, NO!!

DON'T FIGHT ME.

But Lis wasn't doing this.

284

KRMMM

It was her.

The witch.

VANISH!

DAMN IT, LIS!

She
woke
up,

relieved,
so relieved,

FLOP

and then she
remembered

288

she
was alone.

WHUMP

This wasn't
Max. This was
an inanimate
object.

And this place...

289

...this place wasn't hers anymore.

THIS WORLD IS QUIET NOW.

The voice came from above.

THIS WORLD...?

THIS KATIE LEFT.

LEFT IT TO ROT.

EACH KATIE LEAVES.

THEY ALL LEAVE.

EVERY REVISION...

...WAS A *WORLD.*

And for one second, Katie understood: each point of light, each junction,

was not just a new time,

but a new place.

Another Seconds. Another Katie.

Every time she woke up it was as a different person.

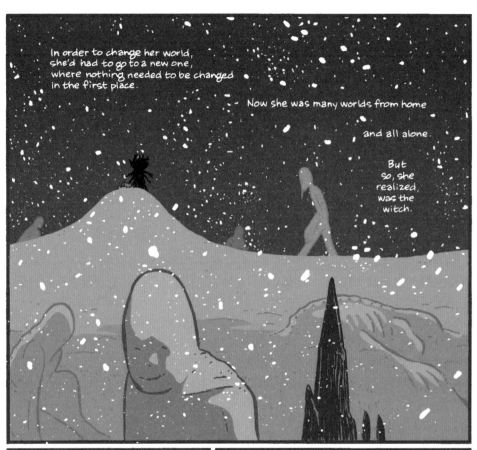

In order to change her world, she'd had to go to a new one, where nothing needed to be changed in the first place.

Now she was many worlds from home

and all alone.

But so, she realized, was the witch.

PLEASE--

LET ME TAKE YOU HOME!

THIS IS HOME NOW.

293

294

ALL OUR CHOICES BROUGHT US HERE.

WE PUSHED PEOPLE AWAY. I ERASED ANDREW! YOU **KILLED** LIS!

NOW LOOK AT US. ALONE *TOGETHER!*

I KNOW YOU'VE HAD IT WORSE. YOU'VE BEEN ALONE FOR A LONG TIME.

A MAGIC MUSHROOM ISN'T GOING TO FIX THAT.

BUT YOU AREN'T ALONE. *I'M HERE NOW.* I'M IN THIS WORLD WITH YOU!

I KNOW IT ISN'T THE GREATEST, BUT WE CAN STILL AT LEAST *TRY* TO MAKE IT A LITTLE BETTER!

DON'T YOU WANT TO TRY?

She returned the pot to its filthy, forgotten fireplace.

She'd done the thing, but she was still freezing her butt off in a dead world.

She had to go back. She had to find Lis. Or at least she had to try.

A piece of Lis's dresser remained. And there she was, curled up inside it like a tiny cat.

304

Katie was hardly shaking anymore.

She gave Lis's last mushroom back.

The cold didn't matter now.

She curled up beside her house spirit

and went to sleep.

She
woke
up.

OH, HEY. WELCOME BACK.

SPOILER WARNING: YOU'RE IN THE HOSPITAL.

WHAT? WHY?

WHY ARE *YOU* HERE? ARE YOU BACK, OR DID YOU EVER LEAVE, OR...?

UH... IN RESPONSE TO YOUR FIRST QUESTION:

YOU PASSED OUT. EXHAUSTION. MALNOURISHMENT, HYPOTHERMIA. THEY SAID ALL THAT WAS IN YOUR STOMACH WAS... MUSHROOMS?

. . .

AND LET ME JUST SAY I'M GENUINELY OFFENDED THAT A CHEF OF YOUR CALIBER WOULD EVER FORGET TO EAT.

SCARED THE SHIT OUT OF ME.

BUT WHERE DID YOU COME FROM? WHAT WORLD IS THIS?

WHAT CHANGED?

WHO'S... WHAT? WHERE'S WHEN?

Arthur just kinda smiled at her and rolled his eyes.

309

UM... HI!

WERE YOU WATCHING ME SLEEP?

FOR LIKE FIVE SECONDS! I JUST WALKED IN!!

HAZEL... YOUR ARMS...

YEAH, I KNOW, GROSS. THEY'RE HEALING, THOUGH!

THEY STILL ITCH AND ACHE. IT'S BEEN A FEW WEEKS NOW...

310

BUT THAT MEANS WE'RE BACK AT THE START.

NOTHING CHANGED.

But

?

something HAD changed.

WAIT.

WHY ARE YOU HERE?

WE'RE FRIENDS.

YEAH, BUT HOW ARE WE FRIENDS?

WE DIDN'T BECOME FRIENDS UNTIL--

--UNTIL YOU TALKED TO ME?

?

And Hazel told her side of the story:

How one day her weird interests unexpectedly became the focus of conversation with a person who had previously seemed intimidating.

An accidental friendship.

Somehow, through all the changes, this one thing had remained.

Maybe she was still feeling weak, but this was a lot for Katie to take. She got a little sobby.

I NEED TO BECOME A BETTER PERSON, ETC.

SHH, IT'S OKAY.

HAZEL... THANKS.

ANY TIME.

UM... YOUR HAND IS KIND OF... SLIMY.

SHIT, SORRY. OINTMENTS AND STUFF.

IT ACTUALLY KINDA HURTS TO TOUCH YOU...

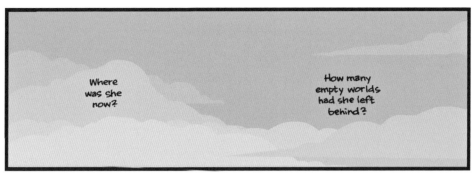

Where was she now?

How many empty worlds had she left behind?

When Arthur drove her home, she wasn't sure what would be waiting for her.

But it was him.

And Katie's life was perfect for just one moment.

314

315

316

That spring, they repainted Seconds for the first time since it opened.

AND IT LOOKS BETTER THAN EVER!

THANK YOU.

Life at the restaurant returned to normal.

BORING OLD NORMAL OLD SECONDS!

Hazel cut her hair,

I LITERALLY CRIED.

and even started to get along with the other girls.

ISN'T IT WEIRD THAT WE ALL HAVE BANGS?

HA HA!

WHY ARE WE SHOWING THIS? THIS HAPPENED ONCE! FOR LIKE A MINUTE!

Just trying to end on a positive note. Settle down.

It was often said that Lucky's had a real energy to it, that there was something special about it.

UH, YEAH: *MY FOOD,* DUH.

And Katie? She was the same old Katie.

I'M STILL PRETTY YOUNG, BUT THANKS.

Still cooking. Still making people happy.

OR AT LEAST TRYING, EVERY DAY!

...still talking to herself.

320

And for years after she moved out of the little
apartment, Katie would drop in a few nights a
week to leave bread on the rafters,

but
she
never
saw
another
house
spirit.

Acknowledgments

There would be no *Seconds* without my team of Jason, Nathan, and Dustin, and without the whole team at Random House/ Ballantine. I have been truly blessed to have all of you with me on this book. All love to my friends and family for all their support during these wild and crazy years. Thanks to Mike S. for providing the recipe in chapter 3—not only did he write it, he actually came to my house and cooked it in front of me, and then we ate it. Additional thanks to Joel and Cory, my food and restaurant consultants, and very special thanks to Heather, Julie, Rosanna, Vili, and Miguel, for helping me to not completely destroy my body during this process.

A Note about the Assistants

Jason Fischer (drawing assistant) is a cartoonist from Los Angeles now living in Portland, Oregon. He loves to draw monsters and food. He enjoys collecting rocks, Daruma dolls, knives, pressed pennies, and Playmobil people.

Nathan Fairbairn (color) is a colorist and writer of comics. He's also a pretty decent cook, despite what his kids might tell you. He lives in Vancouver, Canada.

Dustin Harbin (lettering) is a cartoonist who lives and works in Charlotte, North Carolina. He's too fussy to be a good cook but just fussy enough to be an okay baker.

Additional assistance provided by Megan Messina, Hannah Ayoubi, and Jeremy Arambulo. We love them.

About the Author

Bryan Lee O'Malley is the creator of the bestselling Scott Pilgrim graphic novel series, which was adapted into a major motion picture, *Scott Pilgrim vs. the World,* in 2010. He lives in Los Angeles, where he continues to make comics.